SCHOLASTIC

Maths Practice for

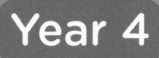

Year 4

Ages 8-9

This book belongs to:

....

Maths Year 4, Book 1

Scholastic Education, an imprint of Scholastic Ltd
Book End, Range Road, Witney, Oxfordshire, OX29 0YD
Registered office: Westfield Road, Southam, Warwickshire CV47 0RA
www.scholastic.co.uk

© 2015, Scholastic Ltd

3 4 5 6 7 8 9   6 7 8 9 0 1 2 3 4 5

British Library Cataloguing-in-Publication Data
A catalogue record for this book is available from the British Library.

ISBN 978-1407-14211-1
Printed in Malaysia

Editorial
Rachel Morgan, Robin Hunt, Kate Baxter,
Lesley Fletcher, Mark Walker

Design
Scholastic Design Team: Neil Salt, Nicolle Thomas
and Oxford Designers & Illustrators Ltd

Cover Design
Neil Salt

Illustration
Aleksander Sotirovski

Contents

Why buy this book?

This series has been designed to support the introduction of the new National Curriculum in schools in England. The new curriculum is more challenging in mathematics and includes the requirement for children's understanding to be secure before moving on. These practice books will help your child revise and practise all of the skills they will learn at school, and including some topics they might not have encountered previously.

How to use this book

- The content is divided into National Curriculum topics (for example, Addition and subtraction, Fractions and so on). Find out what your child is doing in school and dip into the relevant practice activities as required.

- Share the activities and support your child if necessary using the helpful quick tips at the top of most pages.

- Keep the working time short and come back to an activity if your child finds it too difficult. Ask your child to note any areas of difficulty at the back of the book. Don't worry if your child does not 'get' a concept first time, as children learn at different rates and content is likely to be covered throughout the school year.

- Check your child's answers using the answers section at the back of the book.

- Give lots of encouragement and tick off the progress chart as your child completes each chapter.

How to use the book

This tells you which topic you're working on.

This is the title of the activity.

These boxes will help you with the activity.

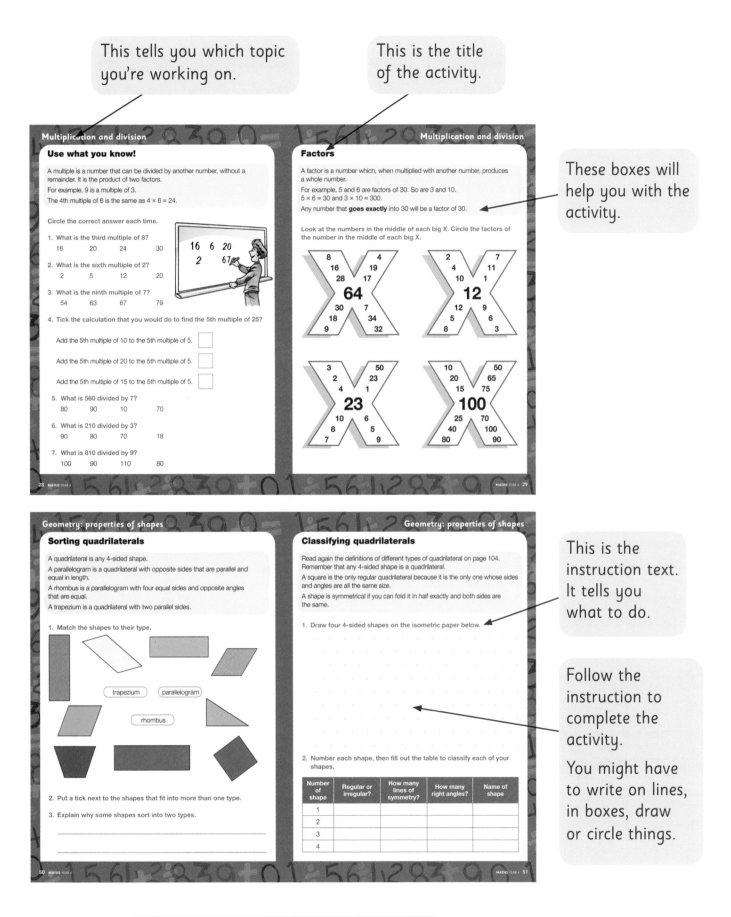

Use what you know!

A multiple is a number that can be divided by another number, without a remainder. It is the product of two factors.

For example, 9 is a multiple of 3.

The 4th multiple of 6 is the same as $4 \times 6 = 24$.

Circle the correct answer each time.

1. What is the third multiple of 8?
   16   20   24   30

2. What is the sixth multiple of 2?
   2   5   12   20

3. What is the ninth multiple of 7?
   54   63   67   79

4. Tick the calculation that you would do to find the 5th multiple of 25?

   Add the 5th multiple of 10 to the 5th multiple of 5. ☐

   Add the 5th multiple of 20 to the 5th multiple of 5. ☐

   Add the 5th multiple of 15 to the 5th multiple of 5. ☐

5. What is 560 divided by 7?
   80   90   10   70

6. What is 210 divided by 3?
   90   80   70   18

7. What is 810 divided by 9?
   100   90   110   80

Factors

A factor is a number which, when multiplied with another number, produces a whole number.

For example, 5 and 6 are factors of 30. So are 3 and 10.

$5 \times 6 = 30$ and $3 \times 10 = 300$.

Any number that **goes exactly** into 30 will be a factor of 30.

Look at the numbers in the middle of each big X. Circle the factors of the number in the middle of each big X.

Sorting quadrilaterals

A quadrilateral is any 4-sided shape.

A parallelogram is a quadrilateral with opposite sides that are parallel and equal in length.

A rhombus is a parallelogram with four equal sides and opposite angles that are equal.

A trapezium is a quadrilateral with two parallel sides.

1. Match the shapes to their type.

   trapezium   parallelogram

   rhombus

2. Put a tick next to the shapes that fit into more than one type.

3. Explain why some shapes sort into two types.

   _____

   _____

Classifying quadrilaterals

Read again the definitions of different types of quadrilateral on page 104. Remember that any 4-sided shape is a quadrilateral.

A square is the only regular quadrilateral because it is the only one whose sides and angles are all the same size.

A shape is symmetrical if you can fold it in half exactly and both sides are the same.

1. Draw four 4-sided shapes on the isometric paper below.

This is the instruction text. It tells you what to do.

Follow the instruction to complete the activity.

You might have to write on lines, in boxes, draw or circle things.

2. Number each shape, then fill out the table to classify each of your shapes.

Number of shape	Regular or irregular?	How many lines of symmetry?	How many right angles?	Name of shape
1				
2				
3				
4				

If you need help, ask an adult!

Counting in 6s, 7s and 9s

Counting in steps of different size helps us to understand number patterns and prepares us for work on times tables.

1	2	3	4	5	**6**	7	8	9	10
11	**12**	13	14	15	16	17	**18**	19	20

6, 12 and 18 are all in the 6s pattern. They are all multiples of 6.

1. **Use a red pencil. Start at 0 and count on 6. Colour the number. Repeat until you have coloured 12 numbers.**

0	1	2	3	4	5	6	7	8	9
10	11	12	13	14	15	16	17	18	19
20	21	22	23	24	25	26	27	28	29
30	31	32	33	34	35	36	37	38	39
40	41	42	43	44	45	46	47	48	49
50	51	52	53	54	55	56	57	58	59
60	61	62	63	64	65	66	67	68	69
70	71	72	73	74	75	76	77	78	79
80	81	82	83	84	85	86	87	88	89
90	91	92	93	94	95	96	97	98	99

a. What is 6 more than:

18 ☐   30 ☐   42 ☐

b. What is 6 less than:

12 ☐   42 ☐   60 ☐

c. Which numbers in the 6-times table are also multiples of 3?

_____

2. **Now use a blue pencil. Start at 0 and count on 7. Colour the number. Count on in steps of 7, until you have coloured 12 numbers.**

a. What is 7 more than:

21 ☐   49 ☐   63 ☐

b. What is 7 less than:

42 ☐   84 ☐   35 ☐

3. **Now use a yellow pencil. Start at 0 and count on 9. Colour the number. Count on in steps of 9 until you have coloured 11 numbers.**

a. What will the 12th number be? ☐

b. What is 9 more than:

18 ☐   36 ☐   63 ☐

c. What is 9 less than:

54 ☐   81 ☐   63 ☐

Counting with negative numbers

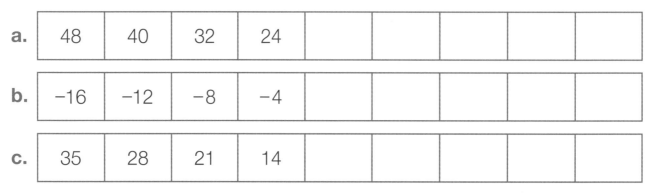

Practise counting on and back from 0 to 20.

Now start at 0 and count backwards, using negative numbers: 0, −1, −2, −3, −4, −5, −6 and so on. Negative numbers are used when reading temperatures: 0 = freezing; −6 is colder than −1 and −6 is less than −1.

1. Complete these sequences.

a.

48	40	32	24				

b.

−16	−12	−8	−4				

c.

35	28	21	14				

2. Fill in the missing numbers on these thermometers.

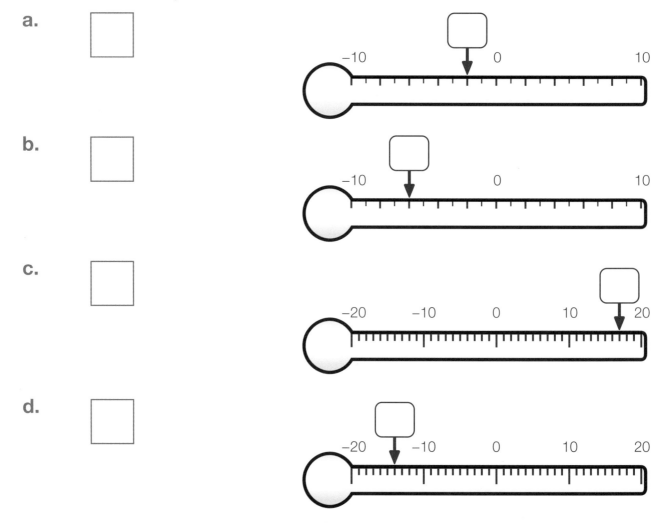

a.

b.

c.

d.

4-digit place value

The position of a number changes its value. Larger numbers need a large number in the 1000s place; smaller numbers need a small number in the 1000s place.

1. **Alex has four number cards: 5, 8, 2 and 7.**

   a. What is the largest number he can make using all four cards?

   _____

   b. What is the smallest?

   _____

2. **Now do the same for these numbers.**

   a. 9 3 4 1:   largest _____   smallest _____

   b. 5 6 5 2:   largest _____   smallest _____

   c. 9 9 8 8   largest _____   smallest _____

   d. 3 0 6 0   largest _____   smallest _____

Ordering numbers

When ordering 4-digit numbers, first look at the 1000s digit; then the 100s, then the 10s and then the 1s.

For example, look at 4672 and 6742. 6742 has the biggest 1000s number, so it is the biggest number.

1. **Answer the following questions by writing 'Yes' or 'No' below.**

    a. Is 1265 more than 1562? _____

    b. Is 29 + 21 equal to 76 − 26? _____

    c. Is 3003 fewer than 3030? _____

    d. Is 7025 more than 7250? _____

    e. Is 5252 smaller than 5225? _____

    f. Is 6074 larger than 6047? _____

2. **Fill in the boxes with the correct sign, < (less than) or > (greater than), so that these number sentences make sense. The first one has been done for you.**

    a. 1654 $\boxed{>}$ 1546

    b. 201 $\boxed{}$ 210

    c. −10 $\boxed{}$ −12

    d. 9242 $\boxed{}$ 9422

3. **Arrange these numbers in order of size, starting with the largest.**

| 6789 | 7896 | 8967 | 6978 | 6987 | 9876 | 7898 |

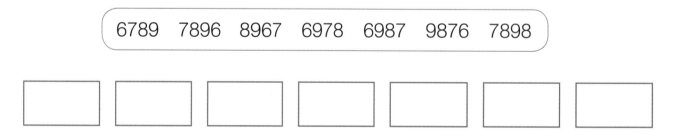

Roman numerals

The Romans used only 7 letters to make numbers. There is no letter for 0.

I	V	X	L	C	D	M
1	5	10	50	100	500	1000

You combine letters to make numbers, such as VI = 6 (5 and 1) and LXVI = 66 (50 and 10, and 5 and 1).

The numbers 4, 9, 40, 90, 400 and 900 are written as subtractions. For example; IV = 4 (5 − 1) with the I before the V to signify one less than that number.

$$9 = IX \ (10 - 1) \quad 40 = XL \ (50 - 10) \quad 90 = XC \ (100 - 10)$$
$$400 = CD \ (500 - 100) \quad 900 = CM \ (1000 - 100)$$

1. **Write the Roman numerals for:**

   a. 2 ☐   b. 7 ☐   c. 19 ☐

   d. 11 ☐   e. 22 ☐   f. 52 ☐

   g. 49 ☐   h. 101 ☐

2. **Fill in the missing Roman numerals on the clock.**

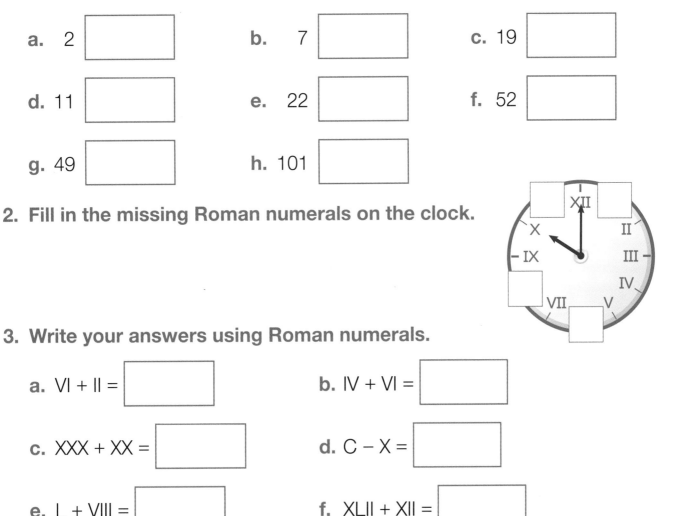

3. **Write your answers using Roman numerals.**

   a. VI + II = ☐   b. IV + VI = ☐

   c. XXX + XX = ☐   d. C − X = ☐

   e. L + VIII = ☐   f. XLII + XII = ☐

Number and place value

4. **Match each number with the correct Roman numeral.**

4	XII
6	XXV
12	CVII
18	XC
25	VI
90	XVIII
107	IV

5. **Add Roman numerals to complete these number sentences. The first one has been done for you.**

a. 5 = **IV** + **I**   b. 10 = [ ] + [ ]

c. 50 = [ ] + [ ]   d. 100 = [ ] + [ ]

e. 500 = [ ] + [ ]   f. 1000 = [ ] + [ ]

6. **Choose the correct word for each sentence.**

> smaller   bigger   0   7

a. Roman numerals use _____ letters to make numbers.

b. There is no symbol for _____.

c. The first letter represents the _____ number.

d. Putting I before X makes it _____.

10, 100 and 1000 more or less

When you add or subtract 10, the 10s number changes.
For example, 40**9**2 − 10 = 40**8**2.

When you add or subtract 100, the 100s number changes.
For example, 4**0**92 + 100 = 4**1**92.

When you add or subtract 1000, the 1000s number changes.
For example, **4**092 − 1000 = **3**092.

1. **Add and subtract 10, 100 and 1000 from each number.**

−1000	−100	−10	Number	+10	+100	+1000
			3040			
			5395			
			7002			
			1256			
			4609			
			6048			
			8794			
			7593			

+1000   +100   +10   −10   −100   −1000

Rounding to the nearest 10

To round to the nearest 10, look at the number of 1s. If there are 5 or more, round up to the next 10. If there are less than 5, round down to the 10 before.

So for 67**3**, **3** is less than 5, so round down: 670.
For 67**8**, **8** is greater than 5, so round up: 680.

1. Round these distances to the nearest 10 kilometres.

    a. 134km _____

    b. 655km _____

    c. 4009km _____

    d. 827km _____

    e. 291km _____

    f. 3913km _____

2. Round these distances from London to the nearest 10 miles.

Town	Distance	Nearest 10 miles
York	209 miles	
Norwich	115 miles	
Leeds	196 miles	
Cardiff	155 miles	
Brighton	53 miles	
Glasgow	405 miles	
New York	3462 miles	

3. Write a number between 0 and 100. It must be nearer to 100 than 0. Place it on the number line.

0   100

Rounding to the nearest 100 and 1000

To round to the nearest 100, look at the 10s digit.

To round to nearest 1000 look at the 100s digit.

Is it 5 or more? Round up. Is it less than 5? Round down.

For example, for 3**6**3: round up to 400. For 4**3**63: round down to 4000.

1. Use the digits to make six 4-digit numbers. Then complete the chart.

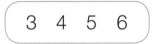

3   4   5   6

My 4-digit number	Round to nearest 100	Round to nearest 1000

2. Bill went to see his local football team play. The local newspaper reported that 3200 people were at the game. This figure was rounded to the nearest 100.

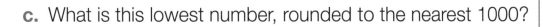

   a. What was the highest number of people that could have been at the game?

   b. What was the lowest number?

   c. What is this lowest number, rounded to the nearest 1000?

Adding and subtracting mentally (1)

To add or subtract several numbers mentally, look for pairs of numbers that total 10, look for near 10s and look for doubles.

For example, to add $8 + 6 + 2 + 5$. $8 + 2 = 10$; $6 + 5$ is a near double (calculate $12 - 1$). So $10 + 11 = 21$.

Work out these problems in your head using the methods above.

- Can you make pairs of numbers that can help you?
- Can you round the numbers to the nearest 10 to help you?
- Can you find doubles or near-doubles?

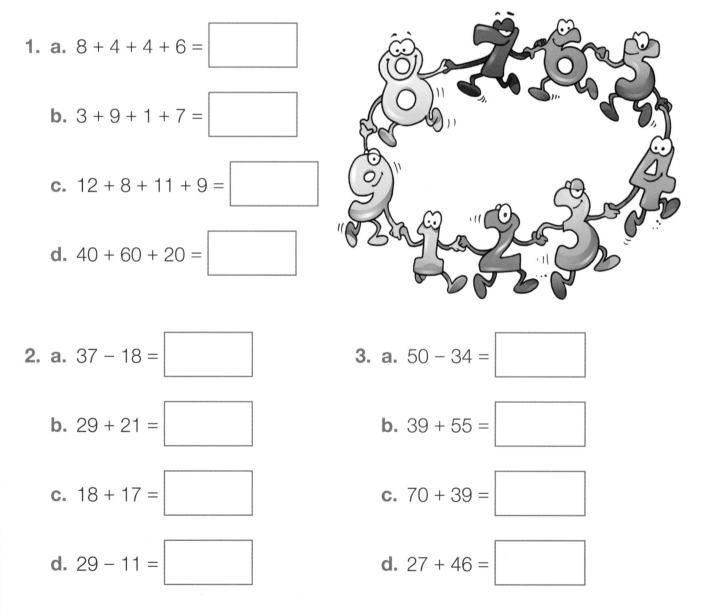

1. a. $8 + 4 + 4 + 6 =$

   b. $3 + 9 + 1 + 7 =$

   c. $12 + 8 + 11 + 9 =$

   d. $40 + 60 + 20 =$

2. a. $37 - 18 =$

   b. $29 + 21 =$

   c. $18 + 17 =$

   d. $29 - 11 =$

3. a. $50 - 34 =$

   b. $39 + 55 =$

   c. $70 + 39 =$

   d. $27 + 46 =$

Adding and subtracting mentally (2)

Using the doubles, multiples of 10 and partitioning numbers can help with mental addition and subtraction. For example:

23 + 8 + 17 + 6 can be partitioned to: 23 + 7 + 10 = 40 and 8 + 6 = 14
so 40 + 14 = 54

Work out these problems in your head using the methods above.

- Can you make pairs of numbers that can help you?
- Can you round the numbers to the nearest multiple of 10 to help you?
- Can you partition the numbers to help you?

1. **a.** 7 + 14 + 5 + 26 =

   b. 34 + 9 + 6 + 11 =

   c. 48 + 12 + 7 + 35 =

   d. 90 + 110 + 60 =

2. **a.** 85 − 28 =

   b. 88 + 41 =

   c. 99 + 88 =

   d. 77 − 49 =

3. **a.** 184 − 62 =

   b. 69 + 47 =

   c. 180 − 52 =

   d. 87 + 66 =

Written strategies for adding

To add horizontally, first add the 1s mentally, then add the 10s mentally. Finally add the 1s and 10s totals mentally. So 27 + 65 = 12 + 80 = 92.

To add using columns, write the sum vertically like this:

```
   6 5
+  2 7
   1 2  (First add the 1s (5 + 7 = 12)
   8 0  Then add the 10s (60 + 20 = 80)
   9 2  Then add to find the total (12 + 80 = 92)
```

1. **Do these sums two ways.**
   - Work horizontally and show your workings.
   - Write the sum vertically. Show your workings.

   The first one has been done for you.

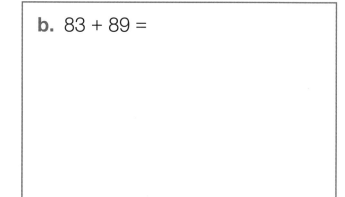

$$37 + 63 = 10 + 90 = 100$$

```
   37
+ 63
   10
   90
  100
```

a. 65 + 45 =

b. 83 + 89 =

c. 123 + 45 =

d. 246 + 78 =

Column skills: addition

To add using columns:

```
  3 7 5
+   5 8
-------
  4 3 3
  1 1
```

Add the 1s column first. Put any 10s below the 10s column to add later.

Add the 10s, including 10s carried from the 1s column. Put any 100s under the 100s column to add later.

Add the 100s, including any 100s carried from the 10s column.

1. **Look at the additions below. Work out the total of the two numbers using the column method. The first one has been done for you.**

	1	4	5	
+		8	9	
	2	**3**	**4**	
	1	1		

a.

	4	5	5	
+		3	9	

b.

	5	7	7	
+		9	9	

c.

	2	3	3	
+		1	8	

d.

	6	8	9	
+		2	7	

e.

	1	6	9	
+		1	9	

f.

	8	9	4	
+		2	8	

Written strategies for subtracting

You can partition numbers to make subtraction easier.

Here is an example:

$$345 \qquad ^{200}\cancel{300} \quad \text{and} \quad ^{130}\cancel{40} \quad \text{and} \quad ^{1}5$$
$$-\underline{76} \qquad \underline{ 70 \ \text{and} \ \ 6}$$
$$\underline{200 \qquad \text{and} \qquad 60 \ \text{and} \ \ 9 = \underline{269}}$$

First work out the 1s, then the 10s, then the 100s.
You may need to exchange 10s or 100s.

1. Practice subtracting numbers using partitioning.

a. 456 – 68 =

b. 631 – 87 =

c. 357 – 89 =

d. 991 – 76 =

e. 436 – 77 =

f. 841 – 75 =

Column skills: subtraction

To subtract using columns:

$$\begin{array}{r} {}^{1}\cancel{2}\,{}^{13}\cancel{4}\,{}^{1}6 \\ -6\,8 \\ \hline 1\,7\,8 \end{array}$$

Subtract the 1s first. For 6 − 8 we need to exchange a 10. 1s become: 16 − 8 = 8. Write 8 in the 1s column.

Subtract the 10s. For 30 − 60 we need to exchange a 100. 10s become: 130 − 60 = 70. Write 7 in the 10s column.

Subtract the 100s. 100 − 0 = 100. Write 1 in the 100s column.

1. **Look at the subtractions below. Using the space provided, set out and work out the answers to the subtraction questions using the column method.**

a. 145 − 89

b. 233 − 14

c. 168 − 19

d. 577 − 98

e. 684 − 27

f. 894 − 28

Estimate and check (1)

To estimate the answer to an addition, you can round both numbers to the nearest 10. Remember: if the 1s are 5 or more, round up; if they are less than 5, round down.

For example, for 36 round up to 40. For 34 round down to 30.

1. Read each question. Use rounding to estimate each sum.

2. Add the numbers mentally to find the actual total.

3. Now write another calculation to check your total is correct.

Question	Estimate of sum	Actual total	Check
18 + 29			
25 + 71			
43 + 78			
92 + 54			
94 + 95			
67 + 84			

Estimate and check (2)

Subtraction is the opposite of addition. It is the inverse operation. We use the inverse operation to check if our calculations are correct. So: 12 + **4** = 16. 16 − 12 = **4**. The numbers in both calculations must be the same.

1. In the second column, write an addition or subtraction number sentence using the two numbers in the first column. Do not write the answer yet.

2. Round each number and estimate the answer to the calculation. Write this in the third column.

3. Check your estimate using an inverse operation. Write this in the fourth column.

4. Now write the actual answer next to the number sentence.

5. Make four more additions and five subtractions, to complete the table.

Numbers	Number sentence and answer	Estimate using rounding	Check using an inverse operation
36, 23	36 + 23 = 59	40 + 20 = 60	60 − 40 = 20
47, 48			
38, 73			
85, 97			
118, 83			
121, 78			
134, 35			
127, 44			
168, 23			
155, 48			
99, 98			

Addition and subtraction money problems (1)

Read each problem. Decide whether it is an addition or subtraction problem. Write the numbers for the calculation in columns, and then work through each column to find the answer.

1. Jamie has been saving his pocket money and has decided to go shopping. Help him decide how to spend it.

a. How much would it cost Jamie to buy the magazine and the model?

_____

b. What is the difference in price between the DVD and the PC game?

_____

c. What is the cost of the DVD and the CD?

_____

d. Jamie decides to buy the model and a magazine and still has £2.55 change. How much did he have to spend altogether?

_____

Addition and subtraction money problems (2)

Read each question and decide which calculation you need to do. Decide which numbers you need in your calculation. Some questions may need more than one calculation.

1. These are the prices of some vegetables.

   Cauliflower £0.90   Potatoes £1.25 per 2.5kg   Carrots £0.60 per kg

   a. I buy one cauliflower, 5kg potatoes and 1kg carrots.
   How much have I spent?

   _____

   b. I have £5. I buy two cauliflowers, 2.5kg potatoes and $\frac{1}{2}$kg carrots.
   How much change do I get?

   _____

2. Jack wants to buy some plants. He buys one tray of plants for £2.50 and one for £3.25. How much change does he get from £10?

   _____

3. Find the total cost of each of these shop transactions A, B and C.

   a.   £ 6 . 5 0   b.   9 9 p   c.   £ 9 . 9 5
       + £ 1 2 . 0 0   + 7 6 p   + £ 0 . 8 8
      _____   _____   _____

4. For each of the transactions above, work out the change received by the customer.

   a. Customer A pays with £20. _____

   b. Customer B pays with £5. _____

   c. Customer C pays with £15. _____

Quick recall ×2 to ×10

Practise saying the 2-, 3-, 4-, 5- and 10-times tables.
Write down any tables facts you cannot recall easily.

1. See how quickly you can complete these questions.

$7 \times \boxed{} = 21$	$\boxed{} \times 4 = 16$	$\boxed{} \times 3 = 12$
$\boxed{} \times 5 = 25$	$6 \times \boxed{} = 30$	$\boxed{} \times 10 = 80$
$9 \times \boxed{} = 27$	$9 \times \boxed{} = 36$	$9 \times \boxed{} = 45$
$\boxed{} \times 4 = 28$	$80 \div 10 = \boxed{}$	$18 \div 2 = \boxed{}$
$36 \div \boxed{} = 9$	$45 \div \boxed{} = 9$	$28 \div 4 = \boxed{}$

Multiplication facts ×2 to ×10

Being able to recall multiplication facts quickly makes written multiplication much easier. Practise saying each times table, to make your recall faster. To fill in a multiplication grid, multiply a top number by a side number. For example, 3 × 2 = 6 and 6 × 2 = 12.

×	3	6
2	6	12

Complete the multiplication grids.

1.

×	2	10	5	1
1				
4				
5				
3				

2.

×	5	6	7	2
3				
6				
4				
5				

3.

×	9	4	6	10
2				
7				
3				
8				

4.

×	5	8	7	3
6				
1				
9				
4				

Use what you know!

A multiple is a number that can be divided by another number, without a remainder. It is the product of two factors.

For example, 9 is a multiple of 3.

The 4th multiple of 6 is the same as 4 × 6 = 24.

Circle the correct answer each time.

1. What is the third multiple of 8?

16   20   24   30

2. What is the sixth multiple of 2?

2   5   12   20

3. What is the ninth multiple of 7?

54   63   67   79

4. Tick the calculation that you would do to find the 5th multiple of 25?

Add the 5th multiple of 10 to the 5th multiple of 5.

Add the 5th multiple of 20 to the 5th multiple of 5.

Add the 5th multiple of 15 to the 5th multiple of 5.

5. What is 560 divided by 7?

80   90   10   70

6. What is 210 divided by 3?

90   80   70   18

7. What is 810 divided by 9?

100   90   110   80

Factors

A factor is a number which, when multiplied with another number, produces a whole number.

For example, 5 and 6 are factors of 30. So are 3 and 10.
5 × 6 = 30 and 3 × 10 = 300.

Any number that **goes exactly** into 30 will be a factor of 30.

Look at the numbers in the middle of each big X. Circle the factors of the number in the middle of each big X.

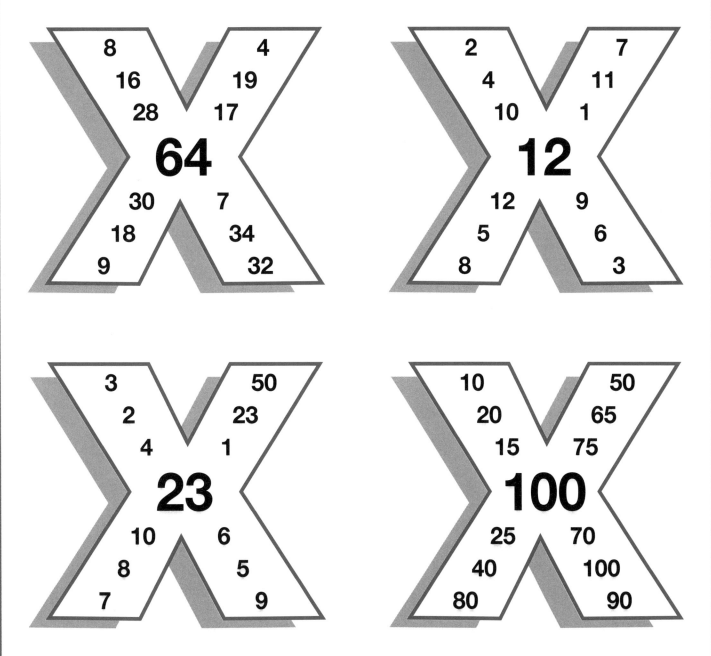

Partitioning when multiplying (1)

Partitioning teen numbers into 10s and 1s can make it easier to multiply. For example, to solve 16 × 7.

16 can be partitioned into **10 + 6**.

We know **10** × 7 = 70 and **6** × 7 = 42. 70 + 42 = 112, so 16 × 7 = 112.

Use multiplication and division facts to work out these calculations. Show your working.

1. 12 × 6 =

Answer =

2. 14 × 5 =

Answer =

3. 17 × 3 =

Answer =

4. 19 × 4 =

Answer =

Partitioning when multiplying (2)

Partitioning numbers into 10s and 1s can make it easier to multiply 2-digit by 1-digit numbers. For example, to solve 42×8.

42 can be partitioned into **40 + 2**.

$40 \times 8 = 320$ and $2 \times 8 = 16$. $320 + 16 = 336$ so $42 \times 8 = 336$.

Use partitioning to work out these calculations. Show your working.

1. $36 \times 5 =$

Answer =

2. $27 \times 4 =$

Answer =

3. $43 \times 8 =$

Answer =

4. $65 \times 6 =$

Answer =

5. $67 \times 7 =$

Answer =

Times-table problems

You can use multiplication facts that you already know to work out others.
For example, to solve 50×3
$50 = 5 \times 10$. So $50 \times 3 = 5 \times 3 \times 10 = 15 \times 10 = 150$.

1. **Work out these questions mentally. Allow five seconds per question.**

   a. $6 \times 7 = $ ☐

   b. $5 \times 8 = $ ☐

   c. $9 \times 3 = $ ☐

   d. $40 \times 7 = $ ☐

   e. $50 \times 6 = $ ☐

   f. $2 \times 90 = $ ☐

2. **I save 80p per week. How much money will I have after 9 weeks?**

   _____

3. **Stickers cost 90p a packet. How much will 6 packets cost?** _____

4. **Chocolate bars are in packets of 6. How many**

   packets do I need to buy for 40 children? _____

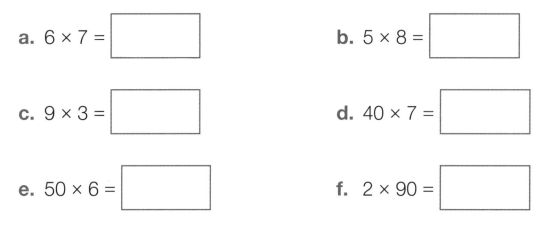

5. **My plant has grown 8cm each week.**

   It is now 32cm tall. How old is it? _____

6. **Answer these questions.**

   a. $56 \div 7 = $ ☐

   b. $64 \div 8 = $ ☐

Multiplying 3 small numbers mentally

You can multiply numbers in any order and the answer will be the same. This is called **commutativity**.

So $3 \times 5 \times 2$ is the same as saying $5 \times 2 \times 3$. The answer is still 30. Rearranging the numbers like this is called the **associative law**.

Use the associative law to help you rewrite and multiply these problems.

1. $6 \times 7 \times 4 =$ _____

2. $8 \times 5 \times 3 =$ _____

3. $9 \times 2 \times 6 =$ _____

4. $10 \times 8 \times 4 =$ _____

5. $3 \times 6 \times 7 =$ _____

6. $8 \times 6 \times 2 =$ _____

7. $4 \times 3 \times 2 =$ _____

8. $5 \times 11 \times 2 =$ _____

9. $7 \times 12 \times 3 =$ _____

Multiplying by 1 and 0

If you multiply a number by 1, the answer will be the same number as the number you are multiplying. For example, $4 \times 1 = 4$ (since 1 lot of 4 = 4).

If you multiply a number by 0, the answer is always 0. For example, $4 \times 0 = 0$ (since 0 lots of 4 = 0).

1. Write the answers to these multiplications.

   a. $6 \times 1 =$

   b. $45 \times 1 =$

   c. $6 \times 4 \times 1 =$

   d. $1 \times 7 \times 5 =$

   e. $450 \times 1 =$

   f. $1 \times 18 =$

   g. $72 \times 1 =$

   h. $2 \times 3 \times 1 =$

   i. $1 \times 12 \times 6 =$

   j. $872 \times 1 =$

2. Now try these.

   a. $1 \times 0 =$

   b. $86 \times 0 =$

   c. $7 \times 3 \times 0 =$

   d. $15 \times 0 =$

   e. $0 \times 240 =$

   f. $11 \times 5 \times 0 =$

3. Hannah bought 1 bag of 50g sweets.

   What was their total mass?

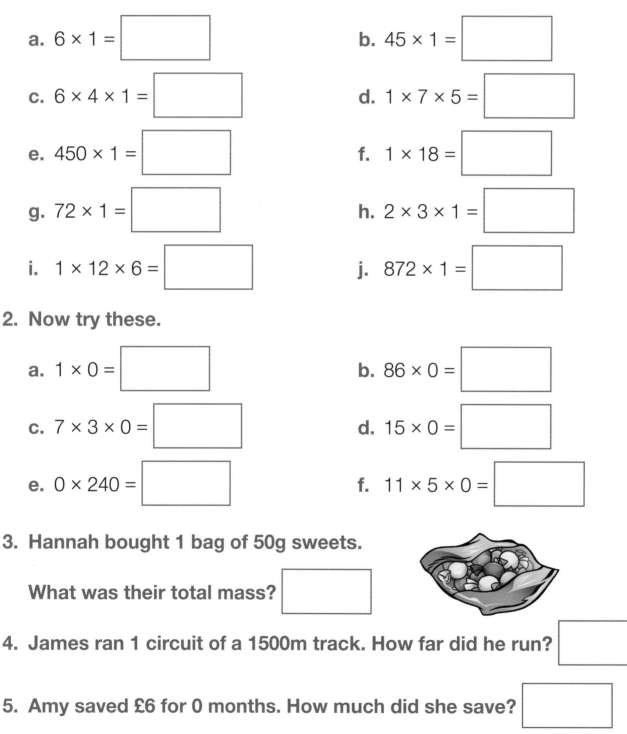

4. James ran 1 circuit of a 1500m track. How far did he run?

5. Amy saved £6 for 0 months. How much did she save?

Dividing by 1

If you divide a number by 1, the answer will always be the same number as the number you are dividing. For example, $6 \div 1 = 6$ (since there are 6 groups of 1 in 6).

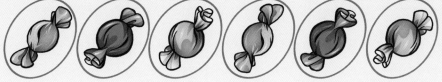

1. **Choose a number from the box. Write it in the table. Divide it by 1 and write the division calculation. Then write your answer. Do this five times.**

6   12   25   49   180   3542

My number	My division	My answer

2. **Fill in the missing numbers.**

   a. $24 \div 1 =$ ☐

   b. ☐ $\div 1 = 750$

   c. $(48 \div 6) \div 1 =$ ☐

   d. $427 \div$ ☐ $= 427$

   e. $(24 \div 2) \div 1 =$ ☐

   f. $(144 \div 12) \div$ ☐ $= 12$

Short multiplication

This is the written method for short multiplication:

$$\begin{array}{r} 8\,3 \\ \times\ \ \ 9 \\ \hline 7\,4\,7 \\ {}_2 \end{array}$$

Multiply the 1s: $3 \times 9 = 27$. Write 7 in the 1s column and write the 2 (10s) under the 10s column.

Multiply the 10s: $8 \times 9 = 72$, then add on the additional 2 underneath = 74. Write 4 in the 10s column and 7 in the 100s column.

1. **Use a written method of short multiplication to solve these problems.**

a. $56 \times 7 =$	**b.** $83 \times 5 =$
c. $35 \times 5 =$	**d.** $72 \times 6 =$

2. **Choose a number from each box. Multiply your numbers together using a written method of short multiplication.**
   Do this three more times.

| 34 76 79 58 | 6 5 4 3 |

Fraction shapes

Count the number of parts in the larger shape (denominator).

Count the number of parts in the smaller shape (numerator).

If there are 5 parts in the larger shape and 2 parts in the smaller shape, the fraction is $\frac{2}{5}$.

1. **Write what fraction the smaller shape is of the larger shape.**

a.

b.

c.

d.

e.

Match equivalent fractions

Equivalent fractions are fractions that have the same value.

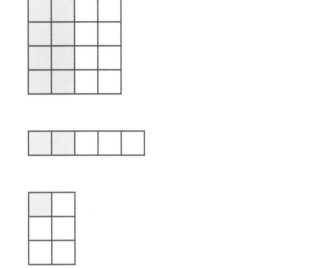 is equivalent to

1. **Draw lines to join the shapes with matching equivalent fractions.**

$\dfrac{4}{10}$

$\dfrac{1}{6}$

$\dfrac{2}{8}$

$\dfrac{2}{12}$

$\dfrac{8}{16}$

$\dfrac{1}{4}$

$\dfrac{2}{5}$

$\dfrac{4}{8}$

Adding and subtracting fractions

To add fractions, add the numerators. The denominator stays the same:
$\frac{4}{7} + \frac{2}{7} = \frac{6}{7}$
To subtract fractions, subtract the numerators. The denominator stays the same: $\frac{4}{7} - \frac{2}{7} = \frac{2}{7}$

1. **Calculate the following.**

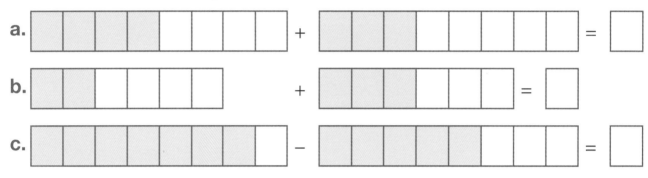

2. **Add or subtract to find each answer.**

a. $\frac{1}{3} + \frac{2}{3} =$ ☐

b. $\frac{2}{7} + \frac{4}{7} =$ ☐

c. $\frac{9}{10} - \frac{4}{10} =$ ☐

d. $\frac{5}{9} - \frac{2}{9} =$ ☐

e. $\frac{3}{5} + \frac{1}{5} =$ ☐

f. $\frac{2}{10} + \frac{6}{10} =$ ☐

g. $\frac{3}{12} - \frac{1}{12} =$ ☐

h. $\frac{6}{6} - \frac{6}{6} =$ ☐

3. **Calculate and then simplify each answer.**

a. $\frac{1}{6} + \frac{2}{6} =$ ☐ $=$ ☐

b. $\frac{1}{8} + \frac{5}{8} =$ ☐ $=$ ☐

c. $\frac{3}{6} + \frac{1}{6} =$ ☐ $=$ ☐

d. $\frac{3}{20} + \frac{5}{20} =$ ☐ $=$ ☐ $=$ ☐

e. $\frac{7}{20} + \frac{8}{20} =$ ☐ $=$ ☐

f. $\frac{23}{100} + \frac{52}{100} =$ ☐ $=$ ☐

g. $\frac{75}{100} - \frac{50}{100} =$ ☐ $=$ ☐

h. $\frac{90}{100} - \frac{30}{100} =$ ☐ $=$ ☐ $=$ ☐

Hundredths

One whole can be divided into 100 parts. Each part is called a **hundredth**.
One hundredth is written as $\frac{1}{100}$ or 0.01.
The position of a digit shows its value. For example, in 562.14 the 4 digit = $\frac{4}{100}$, and 0.14 = $\frac{14}{100}$:

100s	10s	1s	.	0.1s	0.01s
5	6	2	.	1	4

1. **Fill in each small square in the 100-square until you have 100 hundredths.**

$\frac{1}{100}$	$\frac{2}{100}$	$\frac{3}{100}$	$\frac{4}{100}$	$\frac{5}{100}$	$\frac{6}{100}$	$\frac{7}{100}$	$\frac{8}{100}$	$\frac{9}{100}$	$\frac{10}{100}$
$\frac{11}{100}$	$\frac{12}{100}$	$\frac{13}{100}$	$\frac{14}{100}$	$\frac{15}{100}$					
				$\frac{35}{100}$					
						$\frac{47}{100}$			
							$\frac{58}{100}$		$\frac{60}{100}$
$\frac{61}{100}$				$\frac{65}{100}$					
								$\frac{79}{100}$	
	$\frac{82}{100}$								
		$\frac{93}{100}$				$\frac{97}{100}$			

Dividing by 10 and 100

0.6 is 10 times smaller than 6 and 100 times smaller than 60.

60.0 ÷ **10** = 6   The digits have moved **1 place** to the right.

60.0 ÷ **100** = 0.6   The digits have moved **2 places** to the right.

1. Make these amounts 10 and 100 times smaller.

Amount	÷ 10	÷ 100
2780m	278m	
6700km		
£43,000		£430
4060g	406g	
9000p		90p

Amount	÷ 10	÷ 100
2430g		
3000p		
680g		
7500m		
£6000		

2. **Make these amounts 10 times smaller. You might need to add a decimal point.**

a. 8.7 _____   b. 92 _____

c. 36 _____   d. 410 _____

e. 89.7 _____   f. 28.3 _____

g. 8 _____   h. 1.4 _____

i. 701 _____   j. 6.9 _____

3. **Join each number at the top to a number 100 times smaller, below. One has been done for you.**

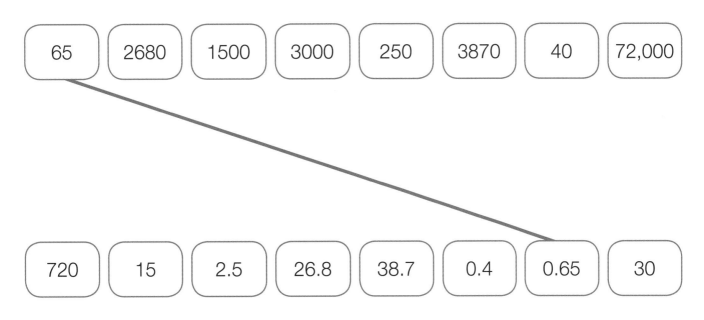

| 65 | 2680 | 1500 | 3000 | 250 | 3870 | 40 | 72,000 |

| 720 | 15 | 2.5 | 26.8 | 38.7 | 0.4 | 0.65 | 30 |

4. **Complete these sentences.**

a. 3.86 is _____ times smaller than 386.

b. 452 is _____ times smaller than 4520.

c. $\frac{1}{10}$ of 365 = _____

d. $\frac{1}{10}$ of 43 = _____

e. $\frac{1}{100}$ of 365 = _____

f. $\frac{1}{100}$ of 43 = _____

g. Class 4 raised £248 in a cake sale. A tenth of this money was spent on

ingredients. How much was this? _____

h. Peter saved 864p. How much is that in pounds and pence? _____

i. Oscar walked 2651cm. How much is that is metres? _____

And in km? _____

Converting lengths

You can record length using different units, such as millimetres (mm), centimetres (cm), metres (m) and kilometres (km).

1. Complete this chart.

	millimetres = 1 centimetre
	centimetres = 1 metre
	metres = 1 kilometre

2. Write the lengths in the new units.

a. 20mm = _____ cm	**b.** 10cm = _____ m
c. 3m = _____ cm	**d.** 200m = _____ km
e. 70cm = _____ mm	**f.** 45cm = _____ mm
g. 6km = _____ m	**h.** 8m = _____ cm
i. 400mm = _____ cm	**j.** 350cm = _____ m

Find the perimeter

The perimeter is the total length around a shape. For a rectangle the perimeter is 2× length + 2× width.

For some shapes, you can split them into two or more rectangles to find the total perimeter.

For some shapes you will need to add the lengths of all the sides.

1. **Find the perimeter of each of these shapes.**

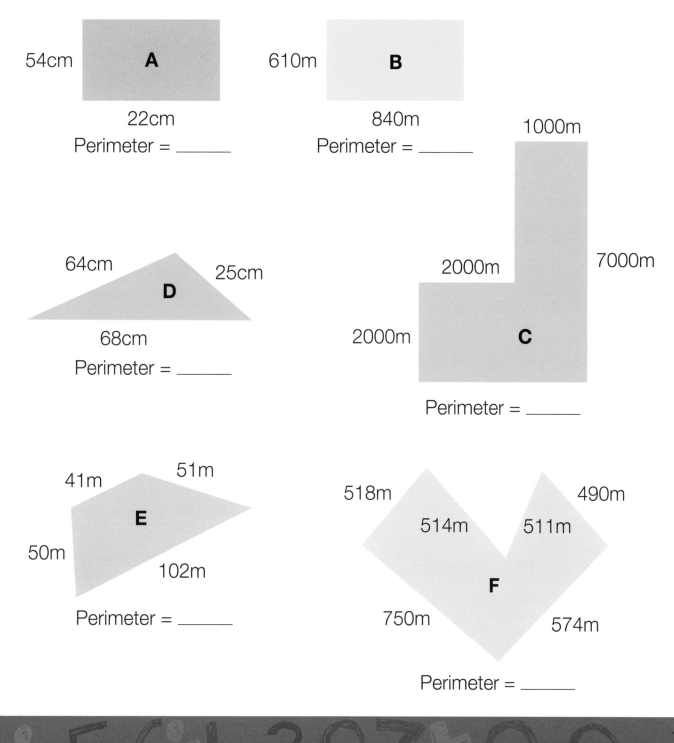

54cm **A**

22cm

Perimeter = _____

610m **B**

840m

Perimeter = _____

64cm **D** 25cm

68cm

Perimeter = _____

1000m

2000m

7000m

2000m **C**

Perimeter = _____

51m

41m **E**

50m

102m

Perimeter = _____

518m 490m

514m 511m

F

750m 574m

Perimeter = _____

Area and perimeter

The area of a rectangle = length × width.
The perimeter of a rectangle is 2× length + 2× width.

Class 4W's classroom needs a new carpet.
Use the plan shown below to answer the questions.
These are two-step problems. Think about what you need to work out first and then how to answer the question.

1. **How much gripper rod do they need for the edge of the carpet?**

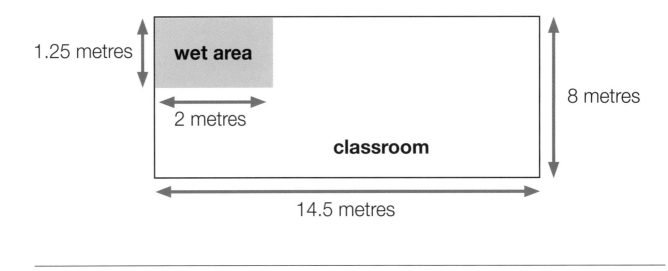

1.25 metres
wet area
2 metres
classroom
8 metres
14.5 metres

_____

_____

2. **How much carpet do they need to cover all of the classroom except the wet area?**

_____

_____

Estimating and measuring capacity

1. Ask an adult for permission and some help to find the capacity of some household items.

   Estimate and measure, in millilitres, the capacity of the following items using water and a measuring jug.

   If you don't have an item on the list, cross it out and write in another, similar item.

   Look at your measuring jug and its scale. Use this to help you estimate the capacity of the other containers.

   Remember: 1000ml = 1 litre 500ml = 0.5 litres 250ml = 0.25 litres

Item	Estimate in millilitres	Capacity in millilitres	Capacity in litres
A cup			
A mug			
A small bowl			
A small saucepan			
An empty carton or tin			

2. Now look in your food cupboard or fridge to see if there are any packets or bottles with the capacity written on them.

   Look for a bottle that holds between 100ml and 500ml.

   Write the details below.

   _____

   _____

Analogue and digital times

To tell the time on an analogue clock:

Look at the long hand
to count the minutes.

Look at the short hand
to find the hour.

Times on a digital clock show the hour and
the number of minutes past the hour.
For example, 2:37 is 37 minutes past 2.

1. **Draw a line to match each analogue clock to the same time on a digital clock.**

12.13

9.08

6.27

5.42

7.36   **3.41**

11.59

6.23

4.24

2.07

Time problems

To find out how many minutes there are in 2 hours 40 minutes, first convert the hours to minutes. Remember, 60 minutes = 1 hour. There are 2 whole hours = 120 minutes. Then add to this number of minutes the 40 minutes you had to start with. 120 minutes + 40 minutes = 160 minutes. So 2 hours 40 minutes = 160 minutes.

Answer these questions and show how you worked them out.

1. There are 60 seconds in one minute. How many seconds are there in five minutes?

_____

_____

2. There are 60 minutes in one hour. How many minutes are there in 3 hours and 50 minutes?

_____

_____

3. How many minutes are there in twelve hours and 30 minutes?

_____

_____

Sorting quadrilaterals

A quadrilateral is any 4-sided shape.

A parallelogram is a quadrilateral with opposite sides that are parallel and equal in length.

A rhombus is a parallelogram with four equal sides and opposite angles that are equal.

A trapezium is a quadrilateral with two parallel sides.

1. **Match the shapes to their type.**

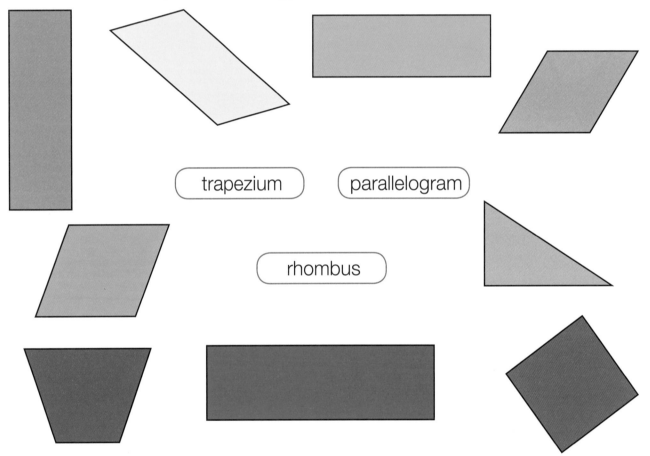

trapezium   parallelogram

rhombus

2. **Put a tick next to the shapes that fit into more than one type.**

3. **Explain why some shapes sort into two types.**

_____

_____

Classifying quadrilaterals

Read again the definitions of different types of quadrilateral on page 50. Remember that any 4-sided shape is a quadrilateral.

A square is the only regular quadrilateral because it is the only one whose sides and angles are all the same size.

A shape is symmetrical if you can fold it in half exactly and both sides are the same.

1. Draw four 4-sided shapes on the isometric paper below.

2. Number each shape, then fill out the table to classify each of your shapes.

Number of shape	Regular or irregular?	How many lines of symmetry?	How many right angles?	Name of shape
1				
2				
3				
4				

Mirror, mirror

1. Complete these shapes by drawing the reflection along the mirror line. You can use a mirror to see the other half of each pattern. Make sure each side is symmetrical.

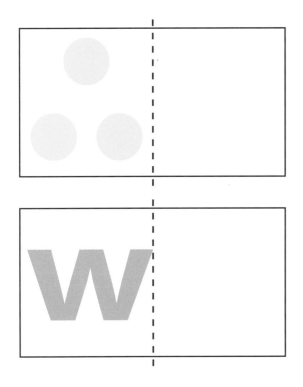

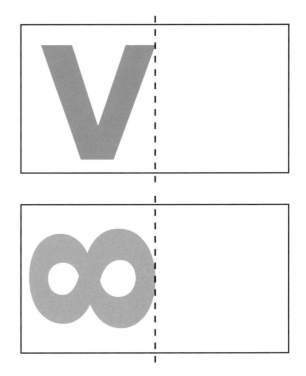

2. Draw the other half of each of these sea creatures. Each half should match exactly.

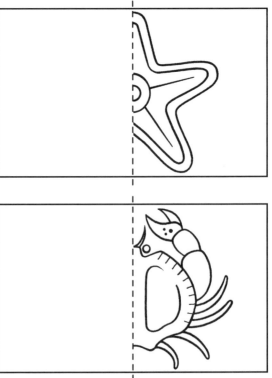

Drawing mirror images

1. Draw the mirror image for each of these.

   Use a mirror and stand it vertically on the line of symmetry to see the mirror image. It will help if you count how many squares from the symmetry line your shape needs to be.

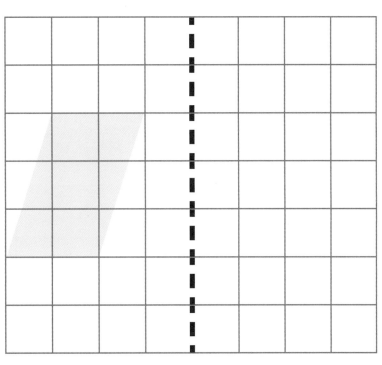

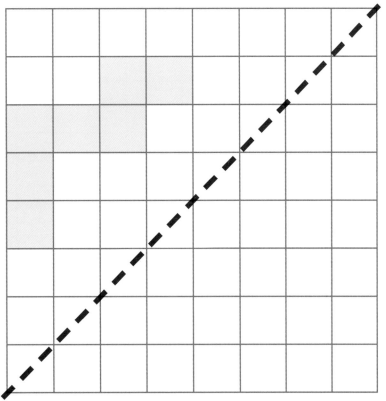

Mystery picture coordinates (1)

To plot a coordinate, such as (5,8), start with the 5: read along the bottom axis until you get to 5. Then read up the left axis until you get to 8. Put a cross where the lines meet. This is the point (5,8).

Remember, first go across, then go up.

1. **Draw a picture by plotting the coordinates and joining each point to the next with a straight line.**

> (1,0); (3,2); (3,5); (3,8); (5,10); (7,8); (7,5); (7,2); (9,0); (7,0); (7,1); (6,1); (6,0); (4,0); (4,1); (3,1); (3,0); join the last point to the first.

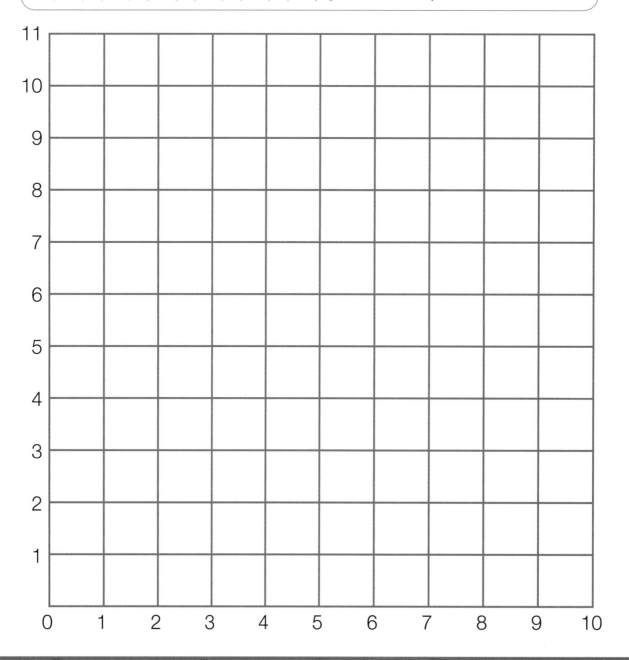

Mystery picture coordinates (2)

Remember, when writing pairs of coordinates, the first number is read along the bottom axis, and the second number is read along the left axis.

1. **Design your own picture. Write down the coordinates for it, so that someone else could draw the picture from your instructions. Each point on your picture will need a new pair of coordinates.**

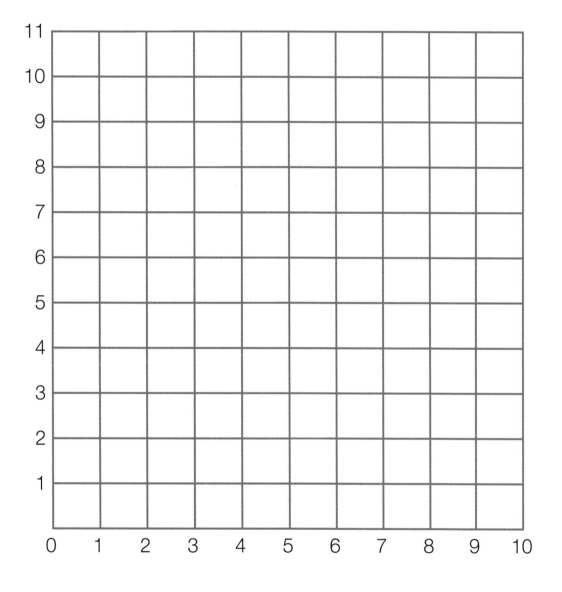

_____

_____

_____

_____

Favourite days bar chart

To understand a bar chart, look at the scale and decide what each rectangle, or part rectangle, represents.

Look at the labels for each axis and the heading of the graph. All this information will help you to answer questions about the bar chart.

Look at this bar chart and answer the following questions.

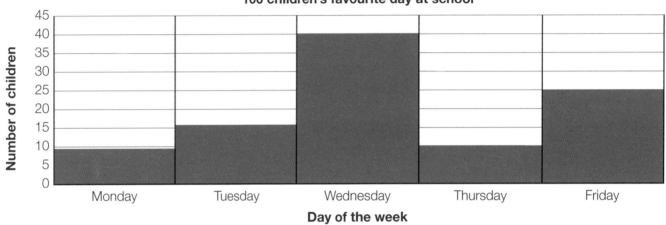

1. How many children took part in the survey? _____

2. What was the favourite day of the week? _____

3. Which day of the week did ten children vote for? _____

4. What is the difference between the number of votes for Thursday and the number of votes for Wednesday?

   _____

5. Why do you think Wednesday could be a popular day of the week?

   _____

6. If 16 children voted Tuesday as their favourite day of the week, how many children voted Monday as their favourite day?

   _____

Drawing a bar chart

The table below shows how many people came to the Lunch Counter restaurant during one week.

Mon	Tues	Wed	Thurs	Fri	Sat	Sun
60	55	15	80	25	90	45

1. Draw a bar chart to show this information. Look at the scale on the bar chart and decide how to represent the information. Write what you think would be the best title for this bar chart.

Title: _____

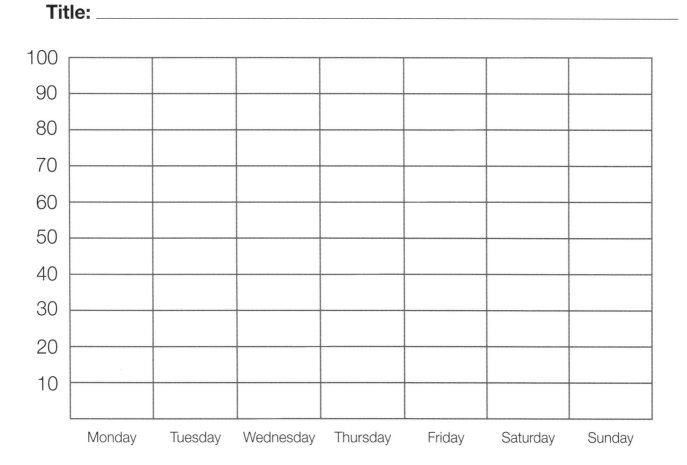

2. On which day did the Lunch Counter have the most customers? _____

3. Which was the least busy day? _____

4. Which two days had a total of 145 customers? _____

5. How many customers were there over the weekend? _____

Interpret information in a time graph

Time graphs show changes in something over a period of time. Look at the scale on the graph to see how much each division is worth.

This time graph shows a baby's weight over 6 months. You could work out the increase each month first to make it easier to answer the questions.

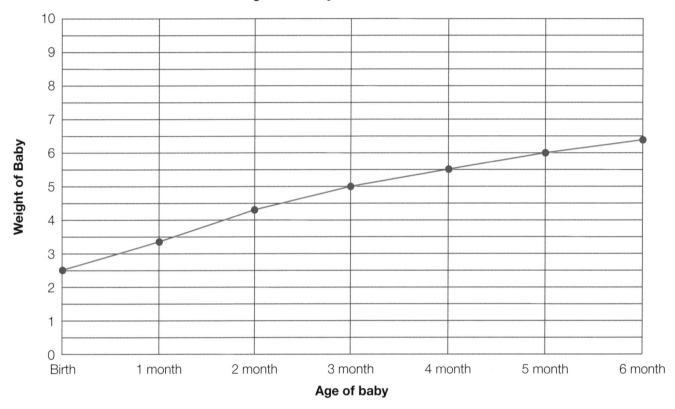

Weight of a Baby 0–6 months.

1. What is the baby's weight at 2 months? _____

2. What was the increase in weight between birth and 3 months? _____

3. Which month showed the greatest increase in weight? _____

4. Which month showed the smallest increase in weight? _____

5. What was the baby's total weight gain during the 6 months? _____

6. The baby does not gain the same amount of weight each month.

   Give a possible explanation for this. _____

Drawing a time graph

To plot the information from this table on a time graph, first find the week at the bottom of your graph and run your finger up the line until it meets the line for the correct number of centimetres. Draw a small cross where the lines meet. You can later join all the crosses to make your line graph.

1. Use the data in the table to create a time graph. Choose the best scale for your graph.

| 1 May | 8 May | 15 May | 22 May | 29 May |

Weeks

Sweet Pea growth during May

Week beginning	1 May	8 May	15 May	22 May	29 May
Height in cm	6	15	22	32	41

2. Which week showed the greatest growth? _____

3. Which week showed the least growth? _____

4. What was the total growth during May? _____

Progress chart

Making progress? Tick (✔) the flower boxes as you complete each section of the book.

Number and place value

Addition and subtraction

Multiplication and division

Fractions

Measurement

Geometry

Statistics

Well done!

YOU DID IT! ★

Name: _____

You have completed **YEAR 4 MATHS** Practice Book

Age: _____   Date: _____

Answers

The answers are given below. They are referenced by page number and where applicable, question number. The answers usually only include the information the children are expected to give.

Page number	Question number	Answers
6–7	1	Numbers coloured in red: 6, 12, 18, 24, 30, 36, 42, 48, 54, 60, 66, 72
	1a	24, 36, 48
	1b	6, 36, 54
	1c	All the numbers that are multiples of 6 are also multiples of 3: 6, 12, 18, 24, 30, 36, 42, 48, 54, 60, 66, 72
	2	Numbers coloured in blue: 7, 14, 21, 28, 35, 42, 49, 56, 63, 70, 77, 84
	2a	28, 56, 70
	2b	35, 77, 28
	3	Numbers coloured in yellow: 9, 18, 27, 36, 45, 54, 63, 72, 81, 90, 99
	3a	108
	3b	27, 45, 72
	3c	45, 72, 54
8	1a	16, 8, 0, –8, –16
	1b	0, 4, 8, 12, 16
	1c	7, 0, –7, –14, –21
	2a	–2
	2b	–6
	2c	17
	2d	–14
9	1a	8752
	1b	2578
	2a	9431, 1349
	2b	6552, 2556
	2c	9988, 8899
	2d	6300, 3600
10	1a	No
	1b	Yes
	1c	Yes
	1d	No
	1e	No
	1f	Yes
	2b	<
	2c	>
	2d	<
	3	6789, 6978, 6987, 7896, 7898, 8967, 9876
11–12	1a	II
	1b	VII
	1c	XIX
	1d	XI
	1e	XXII
	1f	LII
	1g	IL
	1h	CI
	2	I, VI, VIII, XI
	3a	VIII
	3b	X
	3c	L
	3d	XC
	3e	LVIII
	3f	LIV

Page number	Question number	Answers
11–12	4	4 = IV 6 = VI 12 = XII 18 = XVIII 25 = XXV 90 = XC 107 = CVII
	5b	Answers will vary. For example, V + V
	5c	Answers will vary. For example, XXX + XX
	5d	Answers will vary. For example, L + L
	5e	Answers will vary. For example, CD + C
	5f	Answers will vary. For example, D + D
	6a	7
	6b	0
	6c	bigger
	6d	smaller

Page number	Question number	Answers
13	1	_see table below_

–1000	–100	–10	Number	+10	+100	+1000
2040	2940	3030	3040	3050	3140	4040
4395	5295	5385	5395	5405	5495	6395
6002	6902	6992	7002	7012	7102	8002
256	1156	1246	1256	1266	1356	2256
3609	4509	4599	4609	4619	4709	5609
5048	5948	6038	6048	6048	6148	7048
7794	8694	8784	8794	8804	8894	9794
6593	7493	7583	7593	7603	7693	8593

Page number	Question number	Answers
14	1a	130km
	1b	660km
	1c	4010km
	1d	830km
	1e	290km
	1f	3910km
	2	_see table below_

Town	Distance	Nearest 10 miles
York	209 miles	210 miles
Norwich	115 miles	120 miles
Leeds	196 miles	200 miles
Cardiff	155 miles	160 miles
Brighton	53 miles	50 miles
Glasgow	405 miles	410 miles
New York	3462 miles	3460 miles

Page number	Question number	Answers
	3	Accept any number above 51
15	1	_see table below_

My 4-digit number	Round to nearest 100	Round to nearest 1000
3456	3400	3000
3465	3500	3000
3546	3500	4000
3564	3600	4000
3645	3600	4000
3654	3700	4000
4356	4400	4000
4365	4400	4000
4536	4500	5000
4563	4600	5000
4635	4600	5000
4653	4700	5000
5346	5300	5000
5364	5400	5000
5436	5400	5000
5463	5500	5000
6345	6300	6000
6354	6400	6000
6435	6400	6000
6453	6500	6000
6534	6500	7000
6543	6500	7000

Page number	Question number	Answers
	2a	3199
	2b	3150
	2c	3000

Page number	Question number	Answers
16	1a	22
	1b	20
	1c	40
	1d	120
	2a	19
	2b	50
	2c	35
	2d	18
	3a	16
	3b	94
	3c	109
	3d	73
17	1a	52
	1b	60
	1c	102
	1d	260
	2a	57
	2b	129
	2c	187
	2d	28
	3a	122
	3b	116
	3c	128
	3d	153
18	1a	110
	1b	172
	1c	168
	1d	324
19	1a	494
	1b	676
	1c	251
	1d	716
	1e	188
	1f	922
20	1a	388
	1b	544
	1c	268
	1d	915
	1e	359
	1f	766
21	1a	56
	1b	219
	1c	149
	1d	479
	1e	657
	1f	866

Page 22

Question	Estimate of sum	Actual total	Check
18 + 29	50	47	47 – 18 = 29
25 + 71	90	96	96 – 25 = 71
43 + 78	120	121	121 – 43 = 78
92 + 54	140	146	146 – 92 = 54
94 + 95	190	189	189 – 95 = 94
67 + 84	150	151	151 – 84 = 67

Page 23

Numbers	Number sentence and answer	Estimate using rounding	Check using an inverse operation
36, 23	36 + 23 = 59	40 + 20 = 60	60 – 40 = 20
47, 48	47 + 48 = 95	50 + 50 = 100	100 – 50 = 50
38, 73	38 + 73 = 111	40 + 70 = 110	110 – 40 = 70
85, 97	85 + 97 = 182	80 + 100 = 180	180 – 100 = 80
118, 83	118 + 83 = 201	120 + 80 = 200	200 – 120 = 80
121, 78	121 + 78 = 199	120 + 80 = 200	200 – 120 = 80
134, 35	134 + 35 = 169	130 + 40 = 170	170 – 130 = 40
127, 44	127 + 44 = 171	130 + 40 = 170	170 – 130 = 40
168, 23	168 + 23 = 191	170 + 20 = 190	190 – 170 = 20
155, 48	155 + 148 = 303	160 + 150 = 310	310 – 150 = 160
99, 98	99 + 98 = 197	100 + 100 = 200	200 – 100 = 100

Page number	Question number	Answers
24	1a	(Model plane £1.55 and Football magazine 80p) £2.35
	1b	Note variations have been given in case different images are chosen; accept answer so long as calculation is correct. (DVD £3.50 and middle box £2.75) 75p (DVD £3.50 and football image 80p) £2.70
	1c	£5.00
	1d	(Model plane £1.55 and Football magazine 80p) £4.90
25	1a	£4.00
	1b	£1.65
	2	£4.25
	3a	£18.50
	3b	£1.75 or 175p
	3c	£10.83
	4a	£1.50
	4b	325p or £3.25
	4c	£4.17 or 417p

Page 26

$7 \times 3 = 21$ $4 \times 4 = 16$ $4 \times 3 = 12$

$5 \times 5 = 25$ $6 \times 5 = 30$ $8 \times 10 = 80$

$9 \times 3 = 27$ $9 \times 4 = 36$ $9 \times 5 = 45$

$7 \times 4 = 28$ $80 \div 10 = 8$ $18 \div 2 = 9$

$36 \div 4 = 9$ $45 \div 5 = 9$ $28 \div 4 = 7$

Page 27

1.

×	2	10	5	1
1	2	10	5	1
4	8	40	20	4
5	10	50	25	5
3	6	30	15	3

2.

×	5	6	7	2
3	15	18	21	6
6	30	36	42	12
4	20	24	28	8
5	25	30	35	10

3.

×	9	4	6	10
2	18	8	12	20
7	63	28	42	70
3	27	12	18	30
8	72	32	48	80

4.

×	5	8	7	3
6	30	48	42	18
1	5	8	7	3
9	45	72	63	27
4	20	32	28	12

Page number	Question number	Answers
28	1	24
	2	12
	3	63
	4	Child should tick – 'Add the 5th multiple of 20 to the 5th multiple of 5'
	5	80
	6	70
	7	90
29		64 – 4, 8, 16, 32
		12 – 1, 2, 3, 4, 6, 12
		23 – 1, 23
		100 – 10, 20, 25, 50, 100
30	1	72
	2	70
	3	51
	4	76
31	1	180
	2	108
	3	344
	4	390
	5	469

Page number	Question number	Answers
32	1a	42
	1b	40
	1c	27
	1d	280
	1e	300
	1f	180
	2	720p or £7.20
	3	540p or £5.40
	4	7 packets
	5	4 weeks
	6a	8
	6b	8
33	1	168
	2	120
	3	108
	4	320
	5	126
	6	96
	7	24
	8	110
	9	252
34	1a	6
	1b	45
	1c	24
	1d	35
	1e	450
	1f	18
	1g	72
	1h	6
	1i	72
	1j	872
	2a	0
	2b	0
	2c	0
	2d	0
	2e	0
	2f	0
	3	50g
	4	1500m
	5	£0
35	1	Answer will be the same as the chosen number.
	2a	24
	2b	750
	2c	8
	2d	1
	2e	12
	2f	1
36–37	1a	56 × 7 = 392
	1b	83 × 5 = 415
	1c	35 × 5 = 175
	1d	72 × 6 = 432
	2	Answers will vary. For example, 76 × 6 = 456
38	1a	$\frac{2}{4}$ or $\frac{1}{2}$
	1b	$\frac{1}{3}$
	1c	$\frac{2}{6}$ or $\frac{1}{3}$
	1d	$\frac{3}{6}$ or $\frac{1}{2}$
	1e	$\frac{2}{10}$ or $\frac{1}{5}$

Page number	Question number	Answers
39		$\frac{8}{16}$ $\frac{2}{5}$ $\frac{1}{6}$ $\frac{1}{4}$ $\frac{4}{10}$ $\frac{4}{8}$ $\frac{2}{8}$ $\frac{2}{12}$
40	1a	$\frac{7}{8}$
	1b	$\frac{5}{6}$
	1c	$\frac{2}{8}$
	2a	$\frac{3}{3}$ or 1
	2b	$\frac{6}{7}$
	2c	$\frac{5}{10}$
	2d	$\frac{3}{9}$
	2e	$\frac{4}{5}$
	2f	$\frac{8}{10}$
	2g	$\frac{2}{12}$
	2h	$\frac{0}{6}$ or 0
	3a	$\frac{3}{6} = \frac{1}{2}$
	3b	$\frac{6}{8} = \frac{3}{4}$
	3c	$\frac{4}{6} = \frac{2}{3}$
	3d	$\frac{8}{20} = \frac{4}{10} = \frac{2}{5}$
	3e	$\frac{15}{20} = \frac{3}{4}$
	3f	$\frac{75}{100} = \frac{3}{4}$
	3g	$\frac{25}{100} = \frac{1}{4}$
	3h	$\frac{60}{100} = \frac{30}{50} = \frac{3}{5}$
41	1	Hundredths square labelled from $\frac{1}{100} + \frac{100}{100}$

Page number	Question number	Answers

Page 42–43

1

Amount	÷10	÷100	Amount	÷10	÷100
2780m	278m	27.8m	2430g	243g	24.3g
6700km	670km	67km	3000p	300p	30p
£43,000	£4300	£430	680g	68g	6.8g
4060g	406g	40.6g	7500m	750m	75m
9000p	900p	90p	£6000	£600	£60

Question	Answer
2a	0.87
2b	9.2
2c	3.6
2d	41.0
2e	8.97
2f	2.83
2g	0.8
2h	0.14
2i	70.1
2j	0.69

3

65 = 0.65	250 = 2.5
2680 = 26.8	3870 = 38.7
1500 = 15	40 = 0.4
3000 = 30	72,000 = 720

Question	Answer
4a	3.86 is 100 times smaller than 386
4b	452 is 10 times smaller than 4520
4c	$\frac{1}{10}$ of 365 = 36.5
4d	$\frac{1}{10}$ of 43 = 4.3
4e	$\frac{1}{100}$ of 365 = 3.65
4f	$\frac{1}{100}$ of of 43 = 0.43
4g	£24.80 was spent on ingredients.
4h	Peter saved £8.64.
4i	Oscar walked 26.51m; 2.651km.

Page 44

Question	Answer
1	10 millimetres = 1 centimetre
	100 centimetres = 1 metre
	1000 metres = 1 kilometre
2a	2
2b	0.1
2c	300
2d	0.2
2e	700
2f	450
2g	6000
2h	800
2i	40
2j	3.5

Page 45

Question	Answer
1	A = 152cm
	B = 2900m
	C = 20,000m
	D = 157cm
	E = 244m
	F = 3357m

Page 46

Question	Answer
1	45m
2	(8 × 14.5) – (2 × 1.25) = 116 – 2.5 = 113.5m²

Page 47

Question	Answer
1	Answers will vary; check children's measurements.
2	Answers will vary.

Page 48

1

12.13	(clock)	5.42	(clock)
9.08	(clock)	11.59	(clock)
6.27	(clock)	4.24	(clock)
7.36	(clock)	6.23	(clock)
3.41	(clock)	2.07	(clock)

Page 49

Question	Answer
1	300 seconds
2	230 minutes
3	750 minutes

Page 50

1

Question	Answer
2	The two rhombuses and the square should be ticked.
3	The two rhombuses are also parallelograms, since they have two pairs of parallel sides and opposite sides and angles equal.
	The square should also be ticked since squares are both parallelograms and rhombuses: two pairs of parallel sides and all sides and angles equal.

Page 51

Question	Answer
1	Check children's drawings.
2	Answers will vary.

Page 52

Question	Answer
1	Check children's drawings.
2	Check children's drawings.

Page 53

Question	Answer
1	Check children's drawings.

Page 54

1

Page 55

Question	Answer
1	Answers will vary.

Page 56

Question	Answer
1	100
2	Wednesday
3	Thursday
4	30
5	Answers will vary.
6	9

Page 57

1

Number of customers at the lunch counter

Question	Answer
2	Saturday
3	Wednesday
4	Tuesday and Saturday
5	135

Page 58

Question	Answer
1	4.3kg
2	2.5kg
3	Birth to 1 month and 1 month to 2 months: both 0.9kg
4	5 months to 6 months: 0.4kg
5	3.9kg
6	Answers will vary.

Page 59

Question	Answer
1	Check children's drawing.
2	Week of 15 May – 22 May
3	Week beginning 8 May – 15 May
4	35cm